NEVILL
NO-PHONE

ALSO BY ANNA BRANFORD

VIOLET MACKEREL'S BRILLIANT PLOT

VIOLET MACKEREL'S REMARKABLE RECOVERY

First published in Great Britain 2012 by Walker Books Ltd
87 Vauxhall Walk, London SE11 5HJ

2 4 6 8 10 9 7 5 3 1

This book has been typeset in Stempel Schneidler

Printed and bound in Great Britain by Clays Ltd, St Ives plc

British Library Cataloguing in Publication Data:
a catalogue record for this book is
available from the British Library

ISBN 978-1-4063-4402-8

www.walker.co.uk

NEVILLE NO-PHONE

ANNA
BRANFORD

Illustrated by
KAT CHADWICK

WALKER
BOOKS

For Oliver and Téo Alcaraz,
whose mum and dad
appear nowhere in this story. AB

For Coco and Babette. KC

CHAPTER 1

"Dad," I say, "I am the only person in my *whole* class who does not have a mobile phone."

This is not strictly true.

By which I mean at all true.

There is *one* girl in my class who has a mobile phone – Maria Matizzi. It is pink and it has a sparkly fluffy case and when she gets a new message it makes a sort of sprinkling noise and says, "Hey, princess, you have a message!" She brags about it all the time.

There is also Tony Huggins. He reckons he has a mobile phone but he just doesn't want to show it to anyone. We didn't believe him, so one day he brought it to school and it was black with a flip top. But that was the same day that his older brother's phone (which is black with a flip top) went missing and he stomped around the school like an ogre looking for it and Tony hid in the broom cupboard. It was all highly suspicious.

But Dad has no reason to be suspicious, since he does not know the people in my class and they *could* all have their own mobile phones. It is not impossible.

"You don't know what it's like for me, Dad," I say. "Every morning when I arrive at school the kids line up and chant, '*Ne*-ville *No*-phone, *Ne*-ville *No*-phone'."

Of course, this is not strictly true either.

But then I play my best card.

I say, "Do you have any idea what this is doing to my *self-esteem*?"

I'll tell you why this is my best card. A few weeks ago my parents went to a Parent Workshop and Seminar which was held in our school hall and it was called "How to Raise Children with High Self-Esteem". It was all about making kids want to become astronauts and doctors instead of wanting to lie on the couch like my big brother, Dennis, who recently finished Year Ten and now does nothing.

The morning after that seminar my dad said to me, "You know what, Neville? I think you are a great kid. I am so glad that you are *you*."

I said, "Dad, I already took the garbage out."

He said, "No, really, Neville, I just want you to know what a special person I think you are."

I said, "Well, I don't have time to pick up dog poo from the lawn before school."

Thankfully, he gave up after that. So apart from a Post-it note from Mum in my lunch box saying "I believe in you", I didn't hear any more about it. But now I'm wondering if the whole self-esteem thing might actually be quite useful after all.

"I think my *self-esteem* would be a lot higher if I had a mobile phone," I say. "And who knows, that might lead to an improvement in my marks at school and helpfulness around the house and whatnot."

"Neville," says my dad, "you are too young to have a mobile phone and anyway, self-esteem isn't about having things just because other people have them. If everyone in your class jumped off a cliff, would you?"

Actually, if there was a mobile phone at the bottom of the cliff, I would seriously consider it. But I don't say that.

Instead, I say, "I think a mobile phone might help me to *express* myself more."

Last year's Parent Workshop and Seminar was called "How to Raise Children Who Express Themselves" and after attending it, Mum and Dad bought Dennis a saxophone. They must have thought that even though he doesn't like talking to anyone, he might enjoy expressing himself by making a loud tuneless honking sound. He did enjoy it for a week or so, and now it is in the garage collecting dust with the boxing gloves, the chess set, the hockey gear and the telescope.

"Your mother and I will discuss the mobile phone situation," says Dad, "but don't get your hopes up."

I go next door to see how my friend Enzo is getting on. He wants a mobile phone too.

CHAPTER 2

Enzo's parents did not go to the Parent Workshop and Seminar about self-esteem. They did not go to the one about children expressing themselves either. Enzo asked them about the mobile phone almost half an hour ago and they are still laughing.

While we knew there was no way the self-esteem idea would work with Enzo's mum and dad, what they are very keen on is people having jobs. "You're never too young to be useful," is what Enzo's dad says. Enzo says his parents sent him on his first paper round when he was still in nappies, which is probably an exaggeration but not too far from the truth.

So we decided that Enzo should tell his parents that a mobile phone would help him get a better job later on in life, through all the typing practice he would get from sending text messages. He was going to say, "Without a mobile phone I will be disadvantaged in the workplace."

Clearly, it has not worked.

Every so often, his mum and dad stop laughing. Then one of them says, "Disadvantaged in the workplace!" or "Typing practice!" and they both start again. Enzo's mum has tears running down her cheeks from laughing so much and she is saying that it cannot be good for her.

Enzo suggests that we discuss the situation in the privacy of his bedroom.

"So, how did it go?" I ask innocently, and Enzo piffs me with a pillow.

"If I *did* have a mobile phone," he says, "I would use it to call the Society against Unnecessary Meanness and Unfairness to Children."

"I don't think there is one," I say.

"Then I would use it to start one," says Enzo, crossly. "How did it go with your parents?"

"They are considering it," I tell him.

"Lucky."

"I'm not so sure," I say.

You see, I have been caught in this trap before.

My parents once said they were "considering" my request for a go-kart. When I got home from school there was a pile of wood, a hammer and some nails in my room.

"It is empowering for children to *make* their own toys," my dad said. "Just imagine what it will be like for you to have a go-kart that you have built with your own hands."

I said, "Just imagine what it will be like for me to have a go-kart which does not go."

This is how "considering my requests" can sometimes turn out at my house, so you can see why I am suspicious.

"Enzo," I say with great seriousness, "no matter what happens, we must not give up. Humans have walked on the moon. We have built pyramids, cured diseases, invented advanced technological devices, defied gravity. If we really put our minds to it, then some way, somehow, *I believe that we can get a mobile phone.* Are you with me?"

"I'm with you," answers Enzo.

"Say it, Enzo," I order him, as though we are in a movie. "If you're with me, you have to say it."

"*I believe that we can get a mobile phone,*" says Enzo.

Then Mum bangs on Enzo's front door and I have to go home for dinner.

On my way out I make our secret sign, which

you do by making a fist, sticking out your thumb and your little finger, and holding it next to your ear like a phone.

Standing at the top of the stairs, Enzo makes the secret sign back to me.

Enzo's parents have finally stopped laughing but their eyes are still a bit red.

CHAPTER 3

Tonight is Saturday night, which is when Grandma has dinner at our place and it is always cauliflower cheese.

Mum says to Dennis, "If you keep wolfing your food down like that, you will give yourself a stomach-ache."

I eat in small bites, chewing quietly and with my mouth closed for once. When I'm finished chewing, I say, "Mum, have you done something different with the cauliflower cheese tonight? It is unusually delicious."

"It is exactly the same cauliflower cheese we

have every Saturday, Neville," says Mum.

"Interesting," I say. "It is so much nicer than anything I have ever eaten, even in a restaurant."

At an important time like this, you never know what might just tip the scales in your favour.

Dad clears his throat.

"Your mother and I have discussed the possibility of you having a mobile phone and we have a couple of options we would like to suggest."

I cross my fingers under the table. Maybe they are wondering whether I would prefer one with internet access or one with an extendable screen, so I can watch TV shows during recess and then snap it shut to the size of a bus pass.

"Firstly, my old mobile phone is in the garage and you are welcome to have that."

"Dad," I say calmly, "surely you cannot mean the broken one that went through the wash five years ago, then sat out in the backyard in the sun for a few months and is now only in the garage because the dog found it and buried it under a pile of old boxes and newspapers."

"Yes, that one," says Dad.

"Next option," I say.

"When you were a baby," says Mum, "we had a baby monitor which we hooked up to your cot so that we could hear you when you were up in your bedroom and we were downstairs in the kitchen. I know it's not a mobile phone exactly, but it is in a cupboard somewhere and I'm sure I could dig it out if you and Enzo would like to play with it."

I take a deep breath.

"Are there any options which involve me having something that works, that is not covered in old dog drool and that *actually is a mobile phone*?"

"When I was a girl," says Grandma, "we used to play a game using two paper cups and a piece of string. If you connect the cups with the string and pull it taut, you can use it like a telephone."

I grip my fork very tightly.

"Are there any more options?" I ask.

"None that I can think of," says Mum.

"Me neither," says Dad.

"I can think of one," I say brightly. "What if we just go to the shopping centre and *buy* me a mobile phone?"

"When you are sixteen, you can get a part-time job and then you can buy one yourself," says Dad.

"When I am sixteen," I say, "there will be no such thing as a mobile phone. There will be a little sticky hologram chip that you wedge behind your ear so you can communicate using the power of your mind."

"And you will appreciate it all the more because you waited," says Dad.

With the most dignified expression I can muster, I eat all of my cheese and none of my cauliflower. It is my silent protest.

"Tough luck, Tweedledum," says Dennis, who is laughing at me, as usual, with his mouth full. He calls me and Enzo Tweedledum and Tweedledee, which is very annoying. We are ignoring him for now, but one of these days we will take our revenge.

Later on, I go up to my room. My bedroom window faces Enzo's bedroom window and I see him standing there in his pyjamas. I shake my head and give him the thumbs down signal. He shrugs gloomily.

But then he makes the secret sign at me and I make it back at him.

We are not yet defeated. We may still find a way.

CHAPTER 4

The next morning after breakfast Mum asks me to go to the corner shop to get some milk.

"It's definitely just milk we need, Mum?" I ask. "You're quite sure it's only milk?"

"Yes, thank you, Neville, just milk," says Mum.

"Because if you think of anything else after I've gone, you won't be able to call and let me know, since I don't have a mobile phone," I remind her. "If you or Dad or Dennis end up needing some life-saving medicine, for example, I won't be able to find out and get it for you."

"I think we will be all right," says Mum.

"You might be all right," I say, "but what about me? Ever heard of a little thing called stranger danger?" I ask. "And of course there is also a certain issue known as vicious dog attacks. You do realize that if anything goes wrong, there will be no way I can contact you."

"Why don't you ask Enzo if he'll go with you?" suggests Mum. "If you stick together, I am sure you will survive the walk to the corner shop."

"We'll see," I say.

I knock on Enzo's door. I think he is glad of the opportunity to escape. He is in trouble for not cleaning his room and his dad is saying that by the time he was Enzo's age he had already personally built a small village with a well and a farm and was always up before three o'clock in the morning to milk the cows.

We are both quite glum and we half wish that a vicious dog *would* attack us so that our parents would feel guilty for being so unreasonable.

And then, all of a sudden, with no warning at all, we see it.

It is there in the empty bus shelter, just sitting on the seat.

A sleek, black, thin-as-a-comic-book, new-as-a-newsbreak, non-fake, fully functioning mobile phone.

We run towards it in slow motion and when our sweaty hands reach for it, it is like King Arthur reaching for the sword in the stone. We are its rightful owners. We have lived our whole lives so that we might experience this one pure moment. Suddenly, our existence makes perfect sense and the memory of our parents' foolish cruelty falls away like the wrapper of the most delicious chocolate bar that anyone has ever tasted.

My motion is not quite as slow as Enzo's, so my sweaty hands get there first. I am faster only by a nanosecond, but it is enough.

"It's mine," I say firmly.

"It is not yours," says Enzo. "I saw it first. You only saw it because you were watching my eyeballs when *I* saw it."

"I did not," I say. "I never watch people's eyeballs. Actually, I saw it a few minutes ago but I didn't want to say anything in case it got your hopes up."

"Rubbish," says Enzo, "and anyway, you're the one who made up the pledge which was, as you may remember, I believe that we can get a mobile phone. WE. Not YOU. WE."

He has me trapped there. I rack my peabrain for some sort of defence, but there is only one idea in it, which is *stick the mobile phone down your pants and run for it.*

Despite what I said, I look into Enzo's trusting, faithful eyeballs. I find that I cannot betray a friend who has stuck by me through thick and thin. Mostly thin.

"Fine," I say. "We can share the mobile phone."

On the way back home from the corner shop

we take turns holding it up and saying things like, "Sorry, I can't talk now, I have another call coming through," and "No worries, I'll meet you at the corner in five."

We run around in circles.

We laugh like maniacs.

It is like Christmas, a birthday and an amazing dream, all in one.

CHAPTER 5

Enzo and I decide that we will each keep the mobile phone on alternate days and, since I grabbed it first, I will have the first turn. It will be a secret from our families so that nothing can possibly go wrong.

"Neville, you're up to something," says Mum, approximately half a millisecond after I put my foot in the house. "I can tell by the look on your face."

"I haven't had time to get up to anything," I say, "what with buying milk, fighting off strangers and vicious dogs and so on."

"I wasn't born yesterday, you know," she says.

Believe me, I know.

I say, "I don't know what you mean. Although of course my self-esteem has been in shreds lately, so it's possible that the stress has caused me to forget something."

"Such as that rectangular object which you have shoved down your shorts?" asks eagle-eye Mum. She should be one of those people who checks everyone at the airport to make sure they are not trying to smuggle in fireworks or parrots. She would not even need to scan them. She could just use her X-ray vision and interrogation techniques.

"Oh, that," I say. "That's nothing."

"What *sort* of nothing?" asks Mum.

"A surprise!" I say.

"Surprise me," says Mum, grimly.

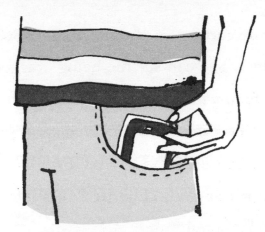

There is no way out of it. I take the mobile phone out of my shorts and lay it lovingly on the kitchen table. "Neville," says Mum, "where did you get that?"

I consider telling her that I stole it off a little old lady before calling her "Wrinkles" and pushing her into a hedge. This small fib is part of a useful technique of Enzo's and mine. She will be so relieved when I tell her the awful story isn't true that she will cope with the *actual* truth much more easily.

But Mum is way ahead of me. My career as

a hardcore criminal is already flashing before her X-ray eyes. She can see me being dragged away from a mobile phone shop in handcuffs.

The headlines in the newspapers will read *LIFE IMPRISONMENT FOR THIEF WITH LOW SELF-ESTEEM DUE TO BAD PARENTING.*

"We found it at the bus stop," I say.

"And what exactly do you plan to do with it?"

"*Share* it with Enzo."

I have a last whisker of hope that this reference to sharing might impress my mum. It does not.

"Neville, that phone belongs to someone. You can't just keep it. You and Enzo will have to find out whose it is and return it to the owner *immediately*."

"How are we supposed to find out?" I ask.

"Look at the phone numbers stored in it," says Dennis, who has come nosily into the kitchen to grab the phone from me with his big gorilla hands. "If you call one of the numbers, someone will be able to tell you whose phone it is." He presses all the buttons with his big gorilla fingers.

But it is brand-new and there are no numbers stored in it.

"You'll have to wait for someone to call then," says Dennis, with his big gorilla voice.

I stomp up the stairs. It is one thing to have a family that refuses to help you with your hopes and dreams. It is another to have a family that actually wants you to hand your hopes and dreams over to total strangers.

I decide to cheer myself up by ringing Enzo to see if there really is a Society against Unnecessary

Meanness and Unfairness to Children. I dial his number on the mobile phone. The soft rubbery buttons click satisfyingly under my fingertips.

"Sorry, you do not have enough credit to make this call," says a strangely robotic female voice, as though it is the best news she has ever heard.

I try again.

She sounds even more thrilled this time.

So despite the sleek and beautiful piece of advanced technology in my pocket, I have to walk round to Enzo's place on my feet like a caveman.

Later in the evening my mum tells Enzo's mum about the mobile phone and we have to listen for about fourteen hours to how we cannot go around just picking things up and keeping them willy-nilly. How would *we* feel if we had lost something precious and someone just kept it, and isn't it time we began to take *responsibility*, et cetera, et cetera. We must be mindful of the value of honesty and of being good citizens who are *respectful* of the property of others and on and on and on all night long.

It is the dreariest evening of our entire lives and we end up having to promise to try to return the phone.

CHAPTER 6

The next morning while we are walking to school, I give the phone to Enzo. It is his turn to have it for the day.

In one way he is lucky since he will instantly become the celebrity of our class, even though the only person whose mobile he could actually call (if we had any credit, which we don't) is Maria Matizzi, and who would want to do that? Not Enzo, I'm pretty sure. She would probably try to invite him to her Pink Fairy Sparkle party.

In another way he is unlucky, and to understand why, you need to know something about our teacher, whose name is Miss Hegarty. Mostly, she is a nice sort of teacher. She only gives out about two detentions every term and she usually feels so sorry for you after all the other kids have gone home that you end up playing tiddlywinks, with a lolly for whoever wins.

But she has this strange thing about bleeping. If there is even the tiniest bleep of *anything* in our classroom, she goes nuts. It is like a normal person turning into a werewolf when the full moon comes out.

To give you an example, at lunchtime a few weeks ago Tony Huggins was timing who could stand on one leg the longest out of Enzo and me. It took so long that the bell rang and we had to go back to class and Tony forgot that the timer part of his watch was still going.

A bit later on Miss Hegarty was explaining how our low marks in spelling don't mean that

we're bad students, just that there is an exciting amount more for us to learn. She was giving everyone a sticker for effort, even Enzo, who was standing on one leg again and definitely not making any effort at all. Then, suddenly, Tony Huggins's watch made a tiny bleep to remind him to turn off the timer. Miss Hegarty's ears swivelled around like a cat's. Her ears do that even if a microwave goes off somewhere down the street. She glares at us even though no one has ever actually brought a microwave to school.

She went straight to Tony Huggins's desk.

"GIVE it to me!" she ordered him.

"It's just my watch," said Tony Huggins. "I was timing Neville and Enz–"

"You were BLEEPING in my classroom," said Miss Hegarty, "which, as you WELL know, is in DIRECT contravention of Section 452, Part 7.98 of the rules of this school. Unless you hand it over

RIGHT NOW, I will have no choice but to inform your parents that you have acted in FLAGRANT disregard for the SPECIFIC regulations regarding inappropriate usage of technological devices in educational settings."

"But I was only–" Tony tried again.

"AND," boomed Miss Hegarty, "I will also be obliged to inform the principal of your BLATANT disrespect for the rules pertaining to wilful and distracting BLEEPING, for which you may face consequences ranging from DETENTION, to SUSPENSION, to EXPULSION."

Tony Huggins's eyes were almost as wide open as his mouth. He undid his watch and gave it to Miss Hegarty, who put it in her desk drawer.

"Thank you, Tony, you may have it back at home time," she said. "Now, did anyone not get a sticker?"

So you can see why Enzo and I are a bit nervous about taking our mobile phone to school. If it rings, nice quiet Miss Hegarty will instantly transform into a raging baboon. But if we miss a call, we might also miss our only opportunity to return the phone to its original owner. Then Enzo's dad will force him to get a volunteer dog-walking job for the good of his character, and my dad will request that the next Parent Workshop and Seminar is called "How to Raise Good Citizens Who Return Lost Property".

Clearly, we need a strategy and this is what we decide on.

At the first hint of even the *beginnings* of a bleep, I will yell as loudly as I can to cover up the sound of ringing. While I am doing that, Enzo will grab the mobile phone from his schoolbag and run to the bathroom in time to answer it and hopefully find out who it belongs to.

It's sure to work. We think.

CHAPTER 7

A bit after recess, when Enzo has finished being the superstar of the whole school for having a mobile phone, everyone is at their desks except for Maria Matizzi. We are doing One-minute Speeches and it is her turn, so she is standing at the front of the classroom talking about her mobile phone as usual. Her speech is about the time her kitten lost its sparkly pink collar but then she rang her sister April on her mobile phone and they bought a new collar which is even pinker and sparklier.

"Thank you for yet another speech about

your mobile phone," says Miss Hegarty. "Does anyone have any questions for Maria?"

Just then, at the back of the classroom where the bags and coats are kept, there is a strange sound. It is a sort of *BOING BOING BOING BOING BOING*.

It takes a moment for my brain to register what it is, as I have been listening out all morning for a *bleep*, not a *boing*. But Miss Hegarty's brain has already begun to register. You can tell by her swivelling ears.

"I HAVE SOME QUESTIONS FOR MARIA," I yell at the top of my lungs. "HOW LONG HAVE YOU HAD YOUR KITTEN AND IS IT A BOY OR A GIRL KITTEN AND DOES IT HAVE LONG HAIR OR SHORT HAIR?"

"Neville, why are you–" begins Miss Hegarty, blinking.

BOING BOING BOING BOING.

"MISS HEGARTY, I NEED TO USE THE BATHROOM," yells Enzo.

"Enzo, please kindly refrain from–" Miss Hegarty tries again.

"WELL, DON'T TAKE TOO LONG, ENZO," I shriek, "BECAUSE OTHERWISE YOU WILL MISS MARIA'S ANSWERS TO MY QUESTIONS AND THAT WOULD BE A PITY."

Enzo has made a run for the bag area and is frantically rummaging through his backpack.

BOING BOING BOING BOING.

"DON'T WORRY, NEVILLE," bawls Enzo, "I'LL BE AS QUICK AS I CAN."

"OKAY," I yell down the corridor after him as he sprints towards the boys' toilets. "IF THERE IS ANY MORE NEWS ABOUT MARIA'S KITTEN, I WILL TELL YOU WHAT SHE SAID AT LUNCH."

"THANKS, NEVILLE. YOU'RE A GOOD FRIEND," bellows Enzo from the other end of the corridor, closing the door of the toilets behind him.

"What on earth was all that about?" asks Miss Hegarty.

"All what about?" I ask innocently.

Miss Hegarty continues to look suspicious and so does Maria Matizzi, since usually Enzo and I make snoring noises while she tells her news. But it seems that Enzo has made it to the boys' toilets without being discovered and that is the main thing.

"So did you find out whose phone it is?" I ask Enzo straightaway at lunchtime.

"I just missed the call," he says gloomily. "But now there's a little envelope in the corner of the screen and it says *1 message received*."

"Voicemail!" I say. "Maybe it says that the

person who left it at the bus stop doesn't actually want it any more and we can just keep it," I suggest. "Maybe the message says *Finders keepers, losers weepers*."

"Maybe," says Enzo, looking a bit doubtful. "But to find out we're going to have to buy some credit."

"It won't cost that much just to listen to one voicemail," I say. "I reckon thirty cents should cover it."

"You reckon?" asks Enzo.

"For a single message?" I say. "Definitely."

CHAPTER 8

After school we walk home via the corner shop.

"We need some phone credit," I tell the man.

"Twenty dollars, thirty dollars or fifty dollars?"

Enzo looks at me.

"We were thinking more like thirty cents," I say.

"Sorry," says the man. "The smallest amount of credit I can sell you is twenty dollars."

We go home to ask for half each.

"Mum," I say, "I need ten dollars in order to be a good citizen who is respectful of the property of others."

"Sorry, Neville," says Mum. "You got yourself into this mess, you can get yourself out of it."

"Dad," Enzo says, when we traipse around to his place, "I need ten dollars to help me appreciate the value of money."

"Then you'll need to work for it," says Enzo's dad.

I have fourteen dollars of leftover birthday money. Enzo has six dollars and fifty cents saved up from the paper runs he has supposedly been doing since he was two.

On our way back to the shop we play the most miserable game in the world, which is called "Things to Spend Twenty Dollars on". Whoever can think of the most fun thing gets to decide what we would definitely have spent the money on if we didn't have to spend it on credit for the mobile phone.

But even though the credit is a depressing waste of our cash, we are actually quite curious to hear the message. When we get back to my place we load the phone up with credit and listen.

All we hear is a giggly voice saying, "Ape, it's Melissa. What's going on? Call me!"

I look at Enzo. He looks at me.

"It could mean that the mobile phone owner is actually an ape," I say. "If so, we can probably keep it."

Enzo looks doubtful.

"Did you say *ape*?" asks Dennis, whose big gorilla ears have been listening in on our conversation. "Lemme hear that."

He grabs the mobile phone from us like it's a banana. He replays the message – *our* message – and then something very strange happens. It is almost as if there is a real human thought going on in his gorilla brain. Maybe he is remembering an ape friend from the jungle where Mum and Dad must have found him before I was born.

"Tell you what," Dennis says. "I'll take that mobile phone off your hands and return it to its owner for you."

"No way," I say. "We just put twenty dollars of our own money onto that thing."

"I'll give you twenty dollars," says Dennis.

"Why?" I ask. "Mum and Dad won't let you keep it either."

"I don't care," says Dennis. "Twenty-five dollars, and that's my final offer."

Enzo looks at me and I give him the nod.

"We'll take it," says Enzo.

Dennis, for some reason only he knows, keeps his money in a sock in one of his drawers. I have a theory that it's because no thief could possibly be brave enough to look inside one of his socks, not even me. Anyway, he comes back with a sock about two-thirds full of five- and ten-cent pieces which he dumps on the end of my bed.

"Can you believe we actually made a profit of five dollars?" asks Enzo as we divide hundreds of mouldy-smelling coins into two neat piles. "Your brother must be pretty stupid to pay twenty-five dollars for a phone he can't keep."

But that's the funny thing. Dennis is sometimes smarter than you'd think from looking at his big gorilla head.

"I'm not so sure," I say. "I think something's going on."

"What kind of something?" asks Enzo.

"The *kind* of something that I bet we can figure out with a bit of careful detective work," I say mysteriously.

CHAPTER 9

Although it is not one of our best detective techniques, Enzo and I begin our investigation by pressing our ears to Dennis's locked door.

There is a brief moment of silence and then, suddenly, the door is yanked open. Enzo and I both nearly fall into Dennis's room (which could easily be fatal, and not just because Dennis gets wild with rage if you use your detective techniques on him, but because the stench can be so overpowering that not even the dog will go in there).

"Well, look, if it isn't Tweedledum and Tweedledee," says Dennis.

"Ah, there you are," I say, thinking quickly. "You overpaid us by five cents, so I wanted to return it to you immediately."

I give him back five cents. It is a small price to pay.

"It has been a pleasure doing business with you," says Enzo, with a slight bow.

Dennis, who in fact underpaid us by fifteen cents, stares at us as we back away slowly. We avoid any sudden movements that might upset a wild animal.

"He's *definitely* up to something," I say to Enzo after we have closed the door.

Enzo nods. "It's almost like 'ape' is code for something that Dennis knows and we don't."

Then my peabrain has a brilliant idea. I go downstairs and find Mum. She is lying on the couch reading a book called *Peaceful Sibling Relationships: 101 creative ways to help your children get along*. She bought it last week after I tried to flush Dennis's *Bikes'n'Chicks* magazine down the toilet because he took the batteries out of my torch and used them up. It ended up with the bathroom flooding and the plumber asking my parents if they were regular readers of *Bikes'n'Chicks*.

"Mum," I say casually. "I was thinking about your helpful suggestion regarding the mobile phone shortage in our home."

"Oh?" says Mum.

"Enzo and I think we might be interested in using the baby monitor after all."

Mum's eagle eyes peer at me for a moment, but she digs it out from the hall cupboard.

"What's that for?" asks Enzo.

"You'll see," I say.

The next part of my plan involves the kitchen. Even the wildest and most dangerous gorillas can be distracted by food. So I set about making the most distracting sandwich the world has ever seen. I take the two softest bits of bread from the very middle of the loaf. I cover them with butter, right up to the edges. I spread some mayonnaise and French mustard on the bottom slice and add a piece of tasty cheddar cheese, a layer of lettuce and tomato, some thin slices of salami, then ham, chicken loaf, cucumber, a few pickles, some finely chopped spring onions and a sprinkling of sea salt and cracked pepper. I top the whole thing off by stabbing it with a toothpick with an olive on the end, like they do if you order a sandwich in an actual restaurant.

Enzo watches me curiously.

"Now, this is the plan," I say. "While I distract Dennis with the sandwich, you have to hide the baby monitor microphone in his room. Then we'll be able to hear any phone conversations he has from the speaker in my room. And *then* maybe we'll be able to solve the Mystery of the Ape."

Enzo gazes at me as though I have just invented the mobile-phone-replacing-chip that you wedge behind your ear so you can communicate using the power of your mind.

For a second I feel quite glad that someone has finally realized what a genius I am, although it turns out that Enzo is only trying to distract me so that *he* can eat the sandwich.

"Cut that out and listen to me," I say. "If the transmitter is hidden in Dennis's room, we'll be able to hear what he's saying in there and maybe that will help us solve the Mystery of the Ape message."

"You know," says Enzo, "that is actually a pretty good idea."

"Thanks," I say.

CHAPTER 10

Operation Baby Monitor is extremely delicate, but we manage it. While Dennis is examining the sandwich for possible tricks, such as a fake rubber slice of cheese or a hidden chilli, Enzo bends down and pretends to do up his shoelace. While he is down there he manages to sneak the transmitter under the bed.

Then, back in my room, we turn on the receiver and listen. Unfortunately, we can only hear the disgusting sound of gorilla eating while Dennis munches his sandwich. Then, before anything interesting can happen, Enzo has to go home and start on his homework. Even though it's not due until the end of the week, his dad says you're never too young to master effective time-management skills that will stand you in good stead later in life.

A little while later, looking through my bedroom window, I can see Enzo, who actually seems to be mastering his comic-reading skills. Just as I am wondering if they will stand him in good stead later in life too, I hear something through the baby monitor. It is difficult to make out at first, but soon my finely tuned detective ears decipher Dennis's voice. He is making a phone call.

"Chaz," he says. "You'll never believe it."

Chaz is Dennis's friend who comes to our house and eats everything in the fridge, including the soy sauce.

"Tweedledum and Tweedledee found a mobile phone and I'm pretty sure it's the one everyone is saying Ape lost. Yes, *the* Ape! There's a message on it from her friend, Melissa!"

I press my ear to the receiver to make sure I don't miss one word. I hear something about "I reckon she's the hottest girl in our suburb" and "A chance like this only comes once in a lifetime".

"So d'you reckon you could get Steve to get Ben to get Melissa to get Ape's home number so I can call her?" Dennis asks Chaz. "Or will she just think I'm an idiot? What would I say to her? *Hi, April. My brother found your new phone. Want to go to a movie so I can give it back to you?* I can't do that!"

I realize that my mouth has been wide open for quite some time. I look like a goldfish with indigestion.

Ape is *April*. And April is a *girl*. My brother Dennis likes a *girl*. He wants to take her to a *movie*. And he is *nervous*. My head is spinning with the shock of it.

"Do you think I should?" he asks, almost begging. "Do you *really* think so?"

The reality of the situation slowly dawns on me. I have found the chink in Dennis's armour, the hole in his money sock, the tick in his gorilla fur. I feel power beginning to surge through my veins. No longer will Dennis be able to make me do his turn of washing up by threatening to tell Mum and Dad that it was me, not the dog, who ate all the chocolate biscuits. No longer will I have to rush out of the shower after only ten seconds because he is banging on the door with his big gorilla fists, yelling, "Hurry up, squirt, or I'll tell Enzo you cried in *The Sound of Music*." Of course, it wouldn't really matter if he did, since I happen to know that Enzo cried in *Bambi*, but that's not the point.

The point, from now on, is that I have discovered Dennis's weakness and therefore *I have the power*. So what if Dennis knows that on stormy nights I still occasionally like to sleep with a stuffed monkey on my pillow? That's nothing compared to *me* knowing that *he* likes a *girl*.

I picture him trying to hog the fish and chips like he usually does. Next time, all I will have

to do is lift one arm up and gently scratch my armpit. To anyone else I will just look like a normal person with an itch. But to my brother it will be a very clear ape-related warning that if there is even one extra chip in his pile, he will be putting up with a whole night *of Dennis and April sitting in a tree, k-i-s-s-i-n-g*.

Just as I am beginning to enjoy another daydream in which I am a great jungle king and Dennis is my small gorilla servant, I see Enzo staring at me from his bedroom. He is probably wondering why I have been grinning and cackling to myself like a maniac for the last ten minutes.

CHAPTER 11

It is too late to ring Enzo's house or run next door to tell him about the amazing discovery, so instead I point to the baby monitor and mime the voice coming out of it. Then I mime a gorilla. Then I mime an ape. Then I mime the gorilla kissing the ape. Then I mime myself enjoying an exact half-portion of fish and chips. Although I think I am actually quite good at mime, for some reason Enzo doesn't seem to understand the message. He shrugs and swirls one finger round and round his ear.

If only Enzo and I had mobile phones (with

credit), I could tell him the news. It is *much* too exciting to wait until tomorrow. But it is also much too exciting to yell between the windows, as I don't want the whole street to hear about my brother's secret (yet). I also don't want Dennis to hear and realize that I have cleverly found him out. And then, with another of my strokes of genius, I remember Grandma's idea about the phone you can make out of cups.

I go down to the kitchen and get two paper cups and a ball of string. I make a small hole in the bottom of each paper cup and cut a piece of string long enough to reach from my bedroom to Enzo's. Enzo watches me curiously from his bedroom as I thread an end of the string into each cup and secure it with a knot.

Now comes the tricky bit. I open my window as wide as it will go and motion for Enzo to do the same. Downstairs our parents are peacefully watching the news with no idea of the ingenious tricks being masterminded above their heads. I have to try about forty-two times to throw one of the paper cups into Enzo's bedroom, but eventually I manage and he catches it.

I hold my cup over my mouth and he puts his cup over his ear.

"Enzo, can you hear me?" I ask him.

Nothing.

I take a couple of steps backwards so that the string is pulled tight and then I try again.

"Can you hear me now?" I ask.

Suddenly, Enzo is nodding and pointing to the paper cup as though it has magically transformed into something else.

I put my cup over my ear and he talks into his.

"How did you know this would work?" he asks, amazed as usual by my genius. His voice buzzes along the string and into my cup and it sounds almost as though he's right next to me.

"That's not important right now," I say. "What I have heard this evening over the baby monitor," I tell him gravely, "may change both of our lives for ever."

I explain the situation to Enzo.

"Are you sure?" he says into his cup. "Are you absolutely certain?"

"Oh, yes," I say. "They don't call me Neville the Great Detective for nothing, you know."

"They don't call you Neville the Great Detective at all," Enzo points out. "They call you Neville Cries-in-*The-Sound-of-Music*-and-cuddles-a-stuffed-monkey."

I hum the theme song from *Bambi* into my cup until Enzo agrees to take this seriously.

Now that we have secret knowledge, somehow we don't mind so much about the mobile phone. Before we go to bed we make up a new secret sign where we lift up one fist and flex our muscles. It means *we have the power*.

CHAPTER 12

The next morning at breakfast, something unusual happens. Dennis speaks. Normally, he just crams food into his big gorilla mouth and makes grunting sounds.

"I won't be in for dinner tonight. I'm going to a movie," he says.

Mum and Dad look at each other with a mixture of slight disbelief and utter joy. I don't know if it is because their firstborn has just uttered two complete sentences in a row or because there might actually be leftovers from dinner for once.

"Taking anyone special? A girl maybe?" asks Mum, trying to sound casual.

Dennis mumbles into his cereal and goes red, which Mum and Dad seem to take as a good sign.

Now is the chance to begin the torment that will last the rest of Dennis's life. I arrange my face into an expression of polite interest.

"I hear *Planet of the APES* is showing in the city," I say. "I think *Tarzan the APE Man* is on too, although it may not start until APRIL."

Dennis glares at me. The cogs in his peabrain are slowly turning. He is wondering how much I know.

"Then there's *Enchanted APRIL, APRIL Showers, Pieces of APRIL*," I continue.

"Don't pester your brother," Dad says to me. "This may be a very important day in his life."

Dennis rolls his eyes, mumbles some more and goes even redder.

"It's not that we don't love you exactly the way you are," says Mum, "but maybe it would be a nice idea to get a haircut before this evening."

Mum has been trying to find ways to make

Dennis get a haircut for months. His hair does look like a sort of helmet made of very thick bristly doormat.

"Maybe," mutters Dennis.

For the rest of the day, strange things continue to happen. First of all, Dennis cleans his shoes. I didn't even know he had shoes. Normally, he just wears enormous stinking flip-flops. Then he irons his trousers. I didn't know he knew how to iron. Normally, he just puts things on straight out of the dryer and they look like an old used tissue.

I give Enzo constant updates using the cup phone.

"Just a minute ago I walked past the bathroom," I say, "and he was cleaning his ears with cotton buds."

"No way," says Enzo.

"He was," I say, "and scrubbing his nails with a nailbrush."

"So what are we going to do?" asks Enzo. His eyes are shining with glee. He has put up with being called Tweedledee ever since he moved next door to us and is keen to have his revenge.

"Maybe we could drop a bucket of water on his head just as he's leaving," suggests Enzo. "Or put itching powder in his pants. Or stick a sign on his back that says *I'm a gorilla.*"

Enzo is right. The possibilities are endless.

I walk past Dennis's room to see what he is doing now. He is on his bed counting change from his sock to see if he has enough for a haircut.

I'm just about to tell him to make sure they shave his gorilla neck too, but something stops me. There is a worried look on his face as he makes small stinking piles of five- and ten-cent pieces that stops me. I've never actually seen my brother look nervous about anything before.

Some cogs seem to start turning in my own peabrain.

Oddly, I begin to find myself thinking about the time he managed to stop Mum and Dad from waving a big sign that said "WE'RE SO PROUD OF YOU" when I got home from school camp. And the time he brought my Spiderman costume to the hospital when I was having my adenoids out when I was six and told the nurses that I was allergic to hospital gowns and would have to wear it for the whole operation, just to cheer me up. And the time we had a mean babysitter who tried to make me go to bed when it was still light outside. Dennis put a pillow in my bed to make it look like I was sleeping and sneaked me out into the garden and we ate an entire family value bag of marshmallows together.

So when he mutters something about borrowing some of the phone money back again, instead of taking the opportunity to make him kneel down and beg me for it, I actually end up giving it to him and also lending him a pair of clean socks so he doesn't have to wear the ones the coins were in.

"Thanks, Neville," he says. He looks slightly less like a gorilla somehow.

CHAPTER 13

We all get the shock of our lives when Dennis gets back from the hairdresser. Mum has been in the back garden trying to find some flowers for him to give to April and Dad has been looking through boxes in the spare room for a book he is sure he once bought called *How to Prepare your Teen for Dating*. I have been busy devising a distraction to keep them both out of the way when April actually arrives so they won't embarrass Dennis. I am tossing up between flooding the bathroom again and telling them that Enzo and I are dropping out of school and joining a gang. Even though it was good fun seeking revenge, I don't mind occasionally using my powers for good. So we are all quite busy and we hardly recognize Dennis when he first walks through the door.

"Dennis!" gasps Mum. "You look so ... handsome!"

Dennis mumbles something.

"Even though appearances are not really important, since it's what's inside that counts," says Dad (who found the book), "you scrub up well, son."

Dennis reddens and mumbles a bit more.

"Hey, Dennis," I say. He looks up. "You look good."

And he does. With his haircut and something a bit like a smile on his face, he hardly seems like a gorilla at all.

While I am upstairs trying to help him flatten

the back of his hair, which has already started to stick up again, the doorbell rings and Mum rushes to answer it while Dad quickly checks the chapter called "What to do and what not to do on your teen's first date". Luckily, it is only Enzo, who is bored of waiting for me to update him on the cup phone and has come round to see what is going on.

"So what's it going to be?" he whispers excitedly. "Bucket of water, itching powder or gorilla sign?"

"Actually, Enzo," I say, "there's been a change of plan."

"I knew it," says Enzo. "We're going to follow them to the cinema and then sit behind them and make gorilla noises right through the movie."

"Not exactly," I say. "Enzo, how would you feel about joining a gang?"

Right then the doorbell rings and this time it really is April. Our house is near the cinema so they are walking there together. Before I can even get to the bathroom to flood it, Mum and Dad rush upstairs and herd Enzo and me into their room.

"We thought it might be nice for Dennis to have some space to greet his date without us making a fuss and without you two pulling any tricks," says Dad.

We all stay up there with our ears pressed against the door until they leave, but none of us can hear anything.

I find it quite peaceful having the place to myself for the evening with Dennis out and Mum and Dad busily reading *So Your Son is Becoming a Man* and sticking Post-it notes beside the important points. Enzo and I spend the time rigging up a pulley between our windows for

passing notes, packets of sherbet, et cetera, back and forth. We also devise a kind of morse code which you do by yanking the string. You don't have to buy credit, there are no *bleeps* or *boings* to get you into trouble and Maria Matizzi can't use it to send you any messages. We think it works pretty well.

Later that night, when Dennis arrives home, Mum and Dad try to be casual. Their idea of being casual is to ask only fifty billion questions instead of five hundred billion.

"Did you have a nice time?" asks Mum.

"I guess," says Dennis.

"Good movie?" asks Dad.

"It was okay," says Dennis.

"Have you had dinner?" asks Mum.

"Yeah," says Dennis.

"What did you have?" asks Dad.

"Food," says Dennis.

"Will you be seeing April again?" asks Mum.

"Dunno," says Dennis.

When he has finally escaped to his bedroom, I knock on the door.

"I'm in bed!" he yells.

"It's me," I whisper.

He opens the door.

"How'd it go?" I ask.

"Good," he says with a non-gorilla smile.

Before I go to bed, I use the new pulley system to send Enzo a dead fly. Even though we still don't have a mobile phone and we didn't even end up taking revenge on Dennis, it's been quite a good day really.

CHAPTER 14

Dennis mustn't have acted too much like a gorilla at the movies because the next day April comes round for morning tea. When I walk past Dennis's bedroom he is already dressed and combing his hair and practising different ways of saying "Would you like some fruit or banana bread?"

When the doorbell rings, Mum and Dad both quickly stop trying to flatten Dennis's bed hair, and find the teapot and start doing very casual things like reading the newspaper and yawning. I sit at the top of the stairs and listen. But when

April comes in she seems to like them and even asks if they grow their own vegetables and what they think about recycling. So they end up acting pretty normal. Dennis looks so relieved that he asks if she'd like some fruit or banana bread in just his regular voice.

Enzo comes round to see what's going on, so we end up sitting with them all for morning tea too.

"April, this is Twee–" begins Dennis, but then he coughs and starts again. "April, this is my brother, Neville, and his friend, Enzo."

"Nice to meet you," says April. "I heard it was actually you two who found my phone."

"Yeah," I say.

"It was nice of you to give it back."

"No worries," I say, not looking at Mum and Dad.

"I have a little sister called Maria who is about your age and she would give anything for a real mobile phone," says April. "I doubt she'd return one if she found it. She has this pink sparkly toy one that says 'Hey princess, you have a message!' every few minutes. It drives everyone mad."

Enzo chokes a bit on his banana bread.

"Maria Matizzi?" I ask. I can feel my eyeballs goggling.

"That's her," says April. "Is she in your class at school?"

"Yeah," I say.

Later on, while Dennis and April are out for a walk, and Mum and Dad are organizing a garage sale to sell the boxing gloves, the chess set, the hockey gear, the telescope, the saxophone and some of their books, Enzo and I go up to my room to discuss the morning tea conversation.

"I can't believe it," says Enzo. "I can't believe we got sucked in by a fake princess phone!"

"I know," I say.

"On Monday we can tell everyone," says Enzo, grinning with glee. "We should make a sign for the classroom door that says FAKE

PHONE FREE ZONE and put pink sparkles on it."

"I guess," I say.

"You guess?" asks Enzo. "Do you have any better ideas?"

"Well," I say, "I'm a bit sick of talking about phones. You know what would be really good?"

"What?" asks Enzo.

"A motorbike."

"As if we could get a motorbike," says Enzo, rolling his eyes.

"Enzo, you are such a quitter," I say. "Humans have walked on the moon. We have built pyramids, cured diseases, invented advanced technological devices, defied gravity. If we really put our minds to it, then some way, somehow, I believe that we can get a motorbike. Are you with me?"

"I'm with you," says Enzo, and we make our new sign, which you do by looking very mean and tough and pretending you are holding handlebars.